Power Squats for Young Minds Vol. I

Logic Grids and Other Puzzles

Shonit Baradia

Published by
Renu Kaul Verma
Vitasta Publishing Pvt Ltd
4348/4C, Ansari Road, Daryaganj
New Delhi - 110 002

वत्स an imprint of Vitasta Publishing

ISBN: 978-81-991712-8-2

First Edition 2025
MRP ₹395

Edited by Saumya
Book Design by Rohit Gautam
Printed by Chaman Enterprises, New Delhi

Contents

Answers

Why Solve Puzzles?

The puzzles in this book aren't just fun, we believe they will also make you smarter. You will:

- **Become a better thinker** – Puzzles improve your problem-solving skills by making you think outside the box.
- **Improve your general knowledge** – Many of the clues in this book rely on general knowledge and trivia, so you'll need to be well-versed in facts before attempting to solve the puzzles.
- **Train your brain** – Finding patterns, searching for connections, and remembering details will boost your memory and focus.
- **Improve confidence** – There's nothing better than the feeling of cracking a tough puzzle; you will feel like a champion!

Welcome to Power Squats for Young Minds Vol 1 — A book with four types of puzzles, each one different and exciting!

1. **LOGIC GRIDS** – Figure out who likes what, who went where, and more! Some clues come as fun riddles or trivia, so you'll need to think carefully before filling in the grid! Kind of like a detective solving a mystery!
2. **SUDOKUS** – Classic number puzzles that test your logic and patience.
3. **CROSSWORD TILES** – A spin on the common crossword where it is all about finding hidden word connections.
4. **WORD SEARCHES** – Can you spot all the hidden words? These are great for sharpening your focus and observation skills!

The puzzles start off easy, but as you go along, they get trickier! Think of it as a puzzle adventure—the more you solve, the better you get. If you ever get stuck, don't give up! Take a break, think it through, and try again.

If you have a question, find a puzzle tricky, or just want to share how much fun you're having, we'd love to hear from you!

You could write to us at shonitb@gmail.com. We read every email and always write back.

So grab a pencil, get comfy, and let the puzzle-solving begin!

Shonit Baradia

Introduction

Logic Grids are a type of logic puzzle where you are given:

- A bunch of categories.
- Each category has options, but each option can be used only once.
- A few clues about these options.

The aim is to use the clues to find which options pair together and form the unique answer.

There are 6 broad types of clues:

- Multi-elimination Clues
- True and False Clues
- Unaligned Pair Clues
- Greater Than/Lesser Than Clues
- Either/Or Clues
- Neither/Nor Clues

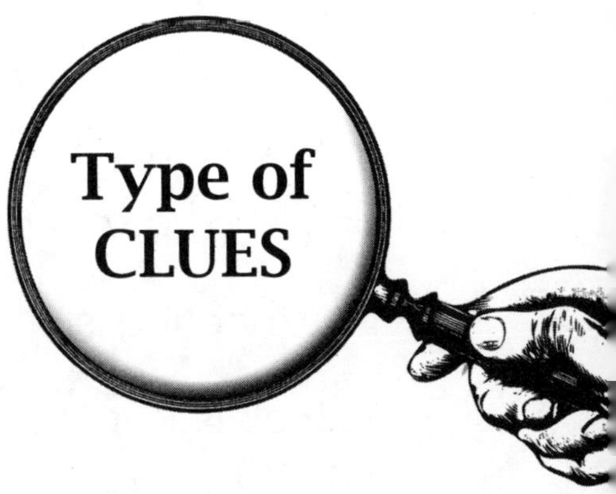

To understand each type of clue, consider the following question:

The five Johnson siblings were sitting around the dinner table and discussing their plans for the following week. Each sibling has a unique profession and coincidentally each sibling has an important meeting the following week in a unique city. Using the clues given below, match each sibling with their profession, the city in which their meeting will take place and the day of the meeting.

1. **Siblings:** Beth, Ed, Josephine, Patrick, Susan
2. **Professions:** Artist, Dancer, Magician, Photographer, Singer
3. **Cities:** Abu Dhabi, Cairo, Pisa, Singapore, Zurich
4. **Days:** Monday, Tuesday, Wednesday, Thursday, Friday

- The five siblings are Patrick; the one who regularly trains their voice; the one who has a meeting at a hotel on the banks of the River Nile; the one who has a meeting on Tuesday and the one who has a meeting on Friday.
- Ed's meeting is on Monday.
- Patrick is not the sibling whose work is usually framed or placed in albums.

- Between Susan and the singer, one sibling has a meeting on Wednesday and the other has a meeting in the capital of the United Arab Emirates.
- The sibling who uses brushes and paint at work has a meeting exactly two days before the meeting in Italy.
- Patrick's meeting will take place after the singer's meeting.
- Susan's meeting will either take place on Tuesday or at a place which is both, a city and a country.
- Neither Patrick nor his sister, the one who performs tricks to amaze her audience, have their meeting in Singapore.
- Neither Josephine nor the photographer have their meeting on Friday.

Note: The target audience for this book is not expected to solve this question. This is a very hard question which is only there to make the reader understand the different types of clues.

Answer

We'll figure out the answer by looking at each clue, making notes and filling in the table when we know how a group and its options are connected.

Name					
Profession					
City					
Day					

Consider Clue #1

The five siblings are Patrick; the one who regularly trains their voice; the one who has a meeting at a hotel on the banks of the River Nile; the one who has a meeting on Tuesday and the one who has a meeting on Friday.

This is a **Multi-elimination Clue.** It lists options from different categories. In this case it lists the five siblings by name, profession, the city in which they have a meeting and the day of their meeting.

So from the clue, the five siblings are:

- Patrick
- The singer (Because a singer needs to train their voice),
- The one who has a meeting in Cairo (Cairo is the only city which lies on the banks of the River Nile),
- The one who has a meeting on Tuesday, and
- The one who has a meeting on Friday

Since each piece of information belongs to a different sibling, we know that can't be mixed up. For example, Patrick can't be the singer or have a meeting in Cairo or on Tuesday or Friday. If a puzzle has a multi-elimination clue, it is best to start with that.

Name	Patrick				
Profession		Singer			
City			Cairo		
Day				Tuesday	Friday

Consider Clue #2 and Clue #3

Ed's meeting is on Monday.

Patrick is not the sibling whose work is usually framed or placed in albums.

These are **True** and **False Clues** which are straightforward. They just tell us if something is true or not.

Clue #2 tells us that Ed and Monday go together. We write this as Ed=Monday (which means if Ed is chosen, then Monday will also be chosen). Also because each option pairs uniquely, Ed can't be with any other day, and Monday can't be with any other sibling. Looking at the table, Ed and Monday can go in either Singer or Cairo columns.

Clue #3 tells us Patrick isn't the photographer (a photographer's work—the photos they take—is usually framed or placed in albums.) and can't be together. We can write this as Patrick≠Photographer. So, in our table, Patrick and Photographer can't be in the same column.

Since we're not sure where to put this information yet, let's continue with the next set of clues and come back to it later.

Name	Patrick				
Profession		Singer			
City			Cairo		
Day				Tuesday	Friday

Clue #2: Ed=Monday

Clue #3: Patrick≠Photographer

Consider Clue #4

Between Susan and the singer, one sibling has a meeting on Wednesday and the other has a meeting in the capital of the United Arab Emirates.

This is an **Unaligned Pair Clue.** It gives us more than one true and false relationship without directly telling us which options go together.

The two false relationships:

- Susan≠Singer
- Wednesday≠Abu Dhabi (Capital of the United Arab Emirates)

It also tells us that:

- Susan=Wednesday or Abu Dhabi,
- Singer=Abu Dhabi or Wednesday.

So, if we find out later that Susan=Wednesday, then Singer=Abu Dhabi and vice versa.

Name	Patrick				
Profession		Singer			
City			Cairo		
Day				Tuesday	Friday

From Clue #2

Ed=Monday

From Clue #3

Patrick≠Photographer

From Clue #4

Susan=Wednesday or Abu Dhabi

Singer=Abu Dhabi or Wednesday

Susan≠Singer and Wednesday≠Abu Dhabi

Consider Clue #5

The sibling who uses brushes and paint at work has a meeting exactly two days before the meeting in Italy.

This is a **Greater Than/Lesser Than Clue**. It tells us the order of two options. In this case it says that the Artist's (an artist uses brushes and paint) meeting is exactly two days before the meeting in Pisa (Pisa is the only option which is in Italy).

So:

- If Artist=Monday, then Pisa=Wednesday,
- If Artist=Tuesday, then Pisa=Thursday, and
- If Artist=Wednesday, then Pisa=Friday.

Also, Artist≠Thursday or Friday and Pisa≠Monday or Tuesday.

Sometimes a Greater Than/Lesser Than Clue can be a bit unclear. In this case, it's exact two days apart. But sometimes, it's not so strict.

Consider Clue #6

Patrick's meeting will take place after the singer's meeting.

This is a **Greater Than/Lesser Than Clue** with some flexibility.

So:

- If Singer=Monday, Patrick=Tuesday, Wednesday, Thursday, or Friday,
- If Singer=Tuesday, Patrick=Wednesday, Thursday, or Friday,
- If Singer=Wednesday, Patrick=Thursday, or Friday, and
- If Singer=Thursday, Patrick=Friday.

Additionally, Singer≠Friday and Patrick≠Monday.

Considering this with what we already know from:

Clue #1: Singer≠Tuesday and

Clue #5: Patrick≠Tuesday or Friday,

We can eliminate some options leaving us with:

If Singer=Monday, Patrick=Wednesday or Thursday, and

If Singer=Wednesday, Patrick=Thursday

Tuesday and Friday have been eliminated as options for Patrick. The second and last possibilities have been eliminated completely since Singer ≠ Tuesday and Patrick ≠ Friday, which means Singer ≠ Thursday.

Name	Patrick				
Profession		Singer			
City			Cairo		
Day				Tuesday	Friday

From Clue #2

Ed=Monday

From Clue #3

Patrick≠Photographer

From Clue #4

Susan=Wednesday or Abu Dhabi

Singer=Abu Dhabi or Wednesday

Susan≠Singer and Wednesday≠Abu Dhabi

From Clue #5

Artist=Monday/Tuesday/Wednesday

Pisa=Wednesday/Thursday/Friday

From Clue #6

Singer=Monday or Wednesday

Patrick=Wednesday or Thursday

Consider Clue #7

Susan's meeting will either take place on Tuesday or at a place which is both, a city and a country.

This is an **Either/Or Clue**. It tells us one true thing and one false thing. In this case the true thing can be one of the two:

- Susan=Tuesday
- Susan=Singapore (Singapore is both, a city and a country).

So, if Susan=Tuesday, then Susan≠Singapore and vice versa.

The false statement is that Tuesday ≠ Singapore, because Susan is either Tuesday or Singapore, but not both.

Name	Patrick				
Profession		Singer			
City			Cairo		
Day				Tuesday	Friday

From Clue #2

Ed=Monday

From Clue #3

Patrick≠Photographer

From Clue #4

Susan=Wednesday or Abu Dhabi

Singer=Abu Dhabi or Wednesday

Susan≠Singer and Wednesday≠Abu Dhabi

From Clue #5

Artist=Monday/Tuesday/Wednesday

Pisa=Wednesday/Thursday/Friday

From Clue #6

Singer=Monday or Wednesday

Patrick=Wednesday or Thursday

From Clue #7

Susan=Tuesday or Singapore

Tuesday≠Singapore

Consider Clue #8 and Clue #9

Neither Patrick nor his sister, the one who performs tricks to amaze her audience, have their meeting in Singapore.

Neither Josephine nor the photographer have their meeting on Friday.

These are **Neither/Nor Clues.** They tell us false things.

From Clue #8

- Patrick≠Singapore
- Magician (magicians perform magic tricks)≠Singapore.

However, this is not all the information that this clue gives. Just as the case was in Either/Or Clues, Patrick ≠Magician.

Additionally, it is important to note that the magician is Patrick's sister which means Magician=Beth, Josephine or Susan.

Likewise, for Clue #9

- Josephine≠Friday
- Photographer≠Friday
- Josephine≠Photographer

Name	Patrick				
Profession		Singer			
City			Cairo		
Day				Tuesday	Friday

From Clue #2

Ed=Monday

From Clue #3

Patrick≠Photographer

From Clue #4

Susan=Wednesday or Abu Dhabi

Singer=Abu Dhabi or Wednesday

Susan≠Singer and Wednesday≠Abu Dhabi

From Clue #5

Artist=Monday/Tuesday/Wednesday

Pisa=Wednesday/Thursday/Friday

From Clue #6

Singer=Monday or Wednesday

Patrick=Wednesday or Thursday

From Clue #7

Susan=Tuesday or Singapore

Tuesday≠Singapore

From Clue #8

Patrick≠Singapore

Magician≠Singapore

Patrick≠Magician

Magician=Beth, Josephine or Susan

From Clue #9

Josephine≠Friday

Photographer≠Friday

Josephine≠Photographer

This is all the information we need to find the answer.

From Clue #4 and Clue #7

Susan=Wednesday or Abu Dhabi

Susan=Tuesday or Singapore

So, this means Susan=Wednesday and Singapore, or Susan=Tuesday and Abu Dhabi.

If Susan=Wednesday and Singapore, then the only way this can be correct is if Susan=Singer but from

Clue #4 we know:

Susan≠Singer

So, Susan≠Wednesday

Therefore, Susan=Tuesday and Abu Dhabi and
Singer=Wednesday.

Then from Clue #6

As Singer=Wednesday, Patrick=Thursday

Name	Patrick			Susan	
Profession		Singer			
City			Cairo	Abu Dhabi	
Day	Thursday	Wednesday		Tuesday	Friday

From Clue #2

Ed=Monday

From Clue #3

Patrick≠Photographer

From Clue #4

Susan=Wednesday or Abu Dhabi ✓

Singer≠Abu Dhabi or Wednesday ✓

Susan≠Singer and Wednesday≠Abu Dhabi ✓

From Clue #5

Artist=Monday/Tuesday/Wednesday ✓

Pisa=Wednesday/Thursday/Friday ✓

From Clue #6

Singer=Monday or Wednesday ✓

Patrick=Wednesday or Thursday ✓

From Clue #7

Susan=Tuesday or Singapore

Tuesday≠Singapore

From Clue #8

Patrick≠Singapore

Magician≠Singapore

Patrick≠Magician

Magician=Beth, Josephine or Susan

From Clue #9

Josephine≠Friday

Photographer≠Friday

Josephine≠Photographer

From Clue #2

Ed=Monday

This leaves us with Cairo=Monday=Ed

From Clue #9

Josephine≠Friday

This means Josephine=Wednesday and Beth=Friday

Name	Patrick	Josephine	Ed	Susan	Beth
Profession		Singer			
City			Cairo	Abu Dhabi	
Day	Thursday	Wednesday	Monday	Tuesday	Friday

From Clue #2

Ed=Monday ✓

From Clue #3

Patrick≠Photographer

From Clue #4

Susan=Wednesday or Abu Dhabi ✓

Singer=Abu Dhabi or Wednesday ✓

Susan≠Singer and Wednesday≠Abu Dhabi ✓

From Clue #5

Artist=Monday/Tuesday/Wednesday

Pisa=Wednesday/Thursday/Friday

From Clue #6

Singer=Monday or Wednesday ✓

Patrick=Wednesday or Thursday ✓

From Clue #7

Susan=Tuesday or Singapore ✓

Tuesday≠Singapore ✓

From Clue #8

Patrick≠Singapore

Magician≠Singapore

Patrick≠Magician

Magician=Beth, Josephine or Susan

From Clue #9

Josephine≠Friday ✓

Photographer≠Friday

Josephine≠Photographer

From Clue #5

Artist=Monday/Tuesday/Wednesday and Pisa=Wednesday/Thursday/Friday

As Singer=Wednesday:

Artist=Monday/Tuesday and Pisa=Wednesday/Thursday

As Artist=Monday or Tuesday, Artist=Ed or Susan

From Clue #3, Clue #9

Patrick≠Photographer

Josephine≠Photographer

Photographer≠Friday

Photographer=Ed or Susan

So, from this we have made our own **Unaligned Pair Clue:**

Ed and Susan=Photographer and Artist.

This means Patrick and Beth=Dancer and Magician.

From Clue #8

Magician=Beth, Josephine or Susan

Therefore Patrick=Dancer and Beth=Magician

Name	Patrick	Josephine	Ed	Susan	Beth
Profession	Dancer	Singer			Magician
City			Cairo	Abu Dhabi	
Day	Thursday	Wednesday	Monday	Tuesday	Friday

From Clue #2

Ed=Monday ✓

From Clue #3

Patrick≠Photographer ✓

From Clue #4

Susan=Wednesday or Abu Dhabi ✓

Singer=Abu Dhabi or Wednesday ✓

Susan ≠Singer and Wednesday≠ Abu Dhabi ✓

From Clue #5

Artist=Monday/Tuesday/Wednesday ✓

Pisa=Wednesday/Thursday/Friday ✓

From Clue #6

Singer=Monday or Wednesday ✓

Patrick=Wednesday or Thursday ✓

From Clue #7

Susan=Tuesday or Singapore ✓

Tuesday ≠Singapore ✓

From Clue #8

Patrick ≠Singapore

Magician≠ Singapore

Patrick≠ Magician

Magician≠Beth, Josephine or Susan

From Clue #9

Josephine≠ Friday

Photographer≠Friday

Josephine≠Photographer

From Clue #8

Patrick ≠Singapore, Beth=Magician≠Singapore

Since Ed=Cairo and Susan=Abu Dhabi,

The only possible option is Josephine=Singapore=Wednesday.

From Clue #5

Artist=Monday/Tuesday and Pisa=Wednesday/Thursday

As Singapore=Wednesday, Pisa=Thursday Artist=Tuesday

As Artist=Tuesday=Susan, Ed=Photographer

Name	Patrick	Josephine	Ed	Susan	Beth
Profession	Dancer	Singer	Photographer	Artist	Magician
City	Pisa	Singapore	Cairo	Abu Dhabi	
Day	Thursday	Wednesday	Monday	Tuesday	Friday

From Clue #2

Ed=Monday

From Clue #3

Patrick ≠ Photographer

From Clue #4

Susan= Wednesday or Abu Dhabi

Singer= Abu Dhabi or Wednesday

Susan≠Singer and Wednesday≠Abu Dhabi

From Clue #5

Artist=Monday/Tuesday/Wednesday

Pisa=Wednesday/Thursday/Friday

From Clue #6

Singer=Monday or Wednesday

Patrick=Wednesday or Thursday

From Clue #7

Susan=Tuesday or Singapore

Tuesday≠Singapore

From Clue #8

Patrick≠Singapore ✓

Magician≠Singapore ✓

Patrick≠Magician ✓

Magician=Beth, Josephine or Susan ✓

From Clue #9

Josephine≠Friday ✓

Photographer≠Friday ✓

Josephine≠Photographer ✓

This leaves the only remaining city of Zurich. So we get the final table as:

Name	Patrick	Josephine	Ed	Susan	Beth
Profession	Dancer	Singer	Photographer	Artist	Magician
City	Pisa	Singapore	Cairo	Abu Dhabi	Zurich
Day	Thursday	Wednesday	Monday	Tuesday	Friday

Crossword Tiles

A Spin on the Traditional Crossword

How to Solve

Each puzzle will have a clue, word count and number of tiles. The clue sets the whole theme for the puzzle. The number of words indicates how many words need to be formed and the tiles must be used to form words that fit within the theme.

Example

Clue: Planets

Word Count : 4

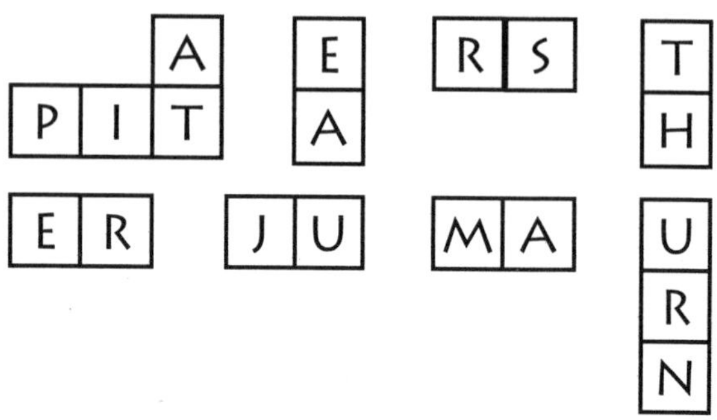

Solution

The clue is **Planets** and the word count is 4. We need to join the tiles such that we form 4 words which relate to the word Planets.

We can join the three horizontal tiles to form **JUPITER** which is the fifth largest planet in our solar system.

We can join the two horizontal tiles to form **MARS** which is the fourth planet in our solar system.

Now we have two words and the following remaining tiles.

We can add two vertical tiles around the 'R' of JUPITER to form EARTH, which is the planet we live on. This gives three out of the four words and the following remaining tiles.

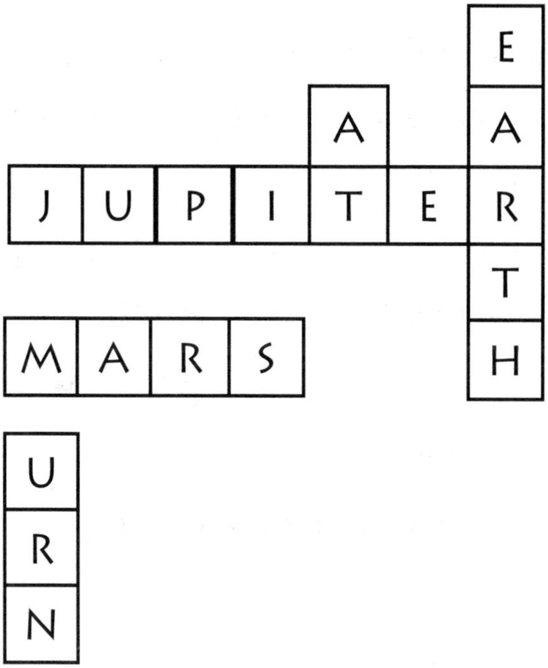

Finally we can join the remaining horizontal below the **AT** to get ATURN.

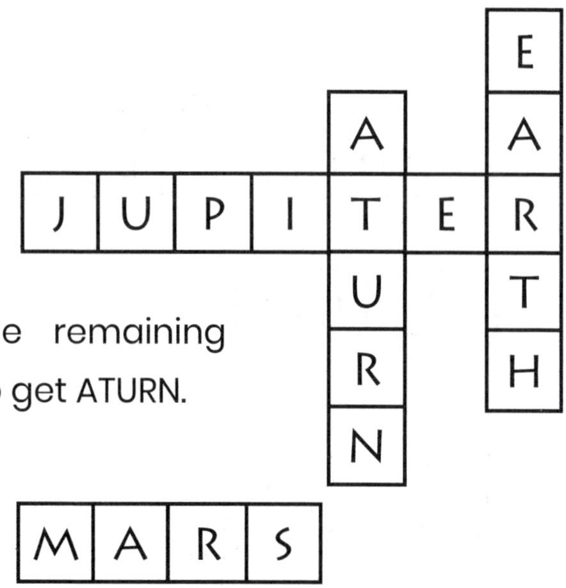

We can now place MARS so that the 'S' is above ATURN to form SATURN, which is the sixth planet in our solar system.

Now we have our four planets and the puzzle is complete.

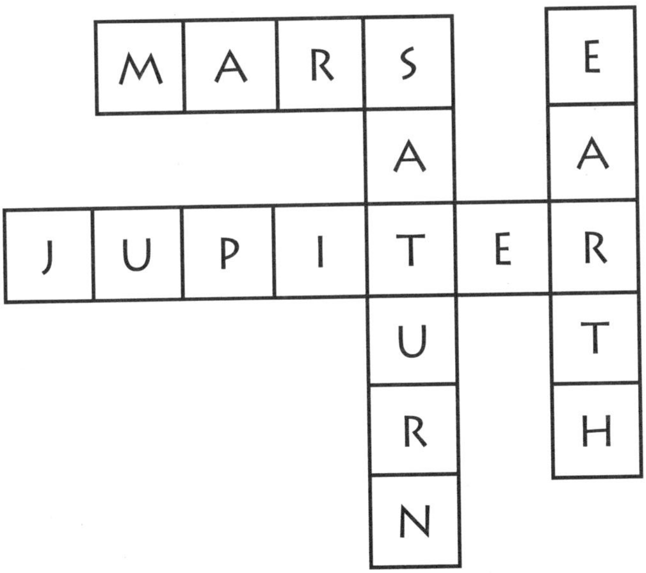

Question 1

Misplaced Order

Three boys go to the movies. Each boy orders a unique flavour of popcorn in a unique size. They are told that their order will be served to them in the auditorium. However, the person who took the order has lost the order sheet. But, he still remembers a few details about their order.

Using the clues given below, match each boy with the correct order.

Clues

Boys	Flavours	Size
Hridaan	Caramel	Small
Lakshya	Cheese	Medium
Jeh	Salted	Large

1. The three boys are: Jeh, the one who ordered salted popcorn and the one who ordered the large size.
2. Hridaan asked for cheese popcorn.
3. The caramel popcorn was not ordered in the smallest size.

Boys			
Flavours			
Size			

Question 2

Milkshakes and Fries

Samaira had a playdate with three of her friends. For snacks, each friend had a milkshake with fries. Each friend had a different milkshake and a different kind of fries.

Using the clues given below, match each friend's pairing of milkshake and fries.

Clues

Friends	Milkshakes	Fries
Alia	Choc Malt	Cheese
Brinda	Vanilla Special	Peri Peri
Chandni	Strawberry Marshmallow	Plain

1. Brinda had the choc malt.
2. The one who had strawberry marshmallow milkshake didn't have the cheese fries.
3. Alia did not have the plain fries.
4. The one who had the vanilla special milkshake had the peri peri fries.

Friend			
Milkshake			
Fries			

Question 3

Red, Blue and Yellow

In a colourful town, there were three best friends named Mr Red, Mr Blue and Mr Yellow. They loved spending time together and always wore clothes and hats of different colours: Red, Blue and Yellow. One sunny day, they decided to meet for lunch.

Using the clues given below, match each person with their clothes and hat colour.

Clues

Friends	Clothes Colour	Hat Colour
Mr Blue	Blue	Blue
Mr Red	Red	Red
Mr Yellow	Yellow	Yellow

1) No one wears the same coloured clothes and hat.
2) Mr Blue doesn't wear a blue hat.
3) Mr Red doesn't wear anything which is red in colour.
4) The one who wears yellow clothes wears a red hat.

Friend			
Clothes Colour			
Hat colour			

#1
Crossword Tiles

Clue: Colours

Word Count: 3

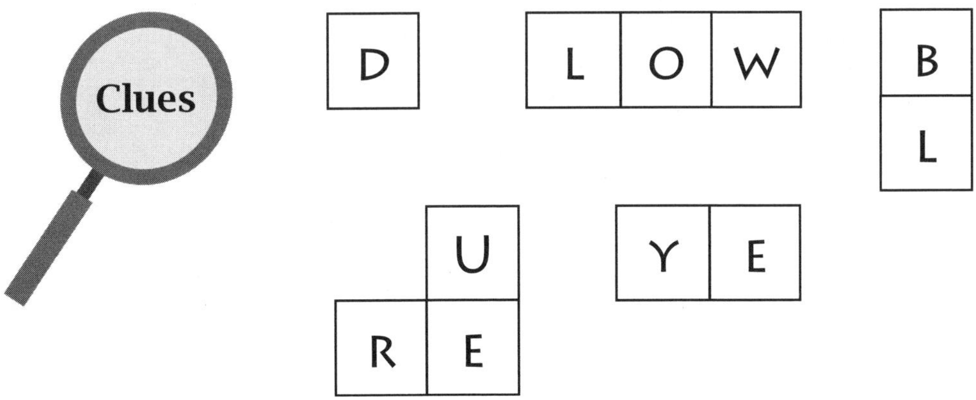

Question 4

Bird Presentation

The Shah family—with mom Mansi, dad Chirag and their three fun-loving kids, Esha, Ishaan and Shanaya—decided to spend an awesome day at Wilderness Trails Nature Park. It was going to be super exciting! After rising up before sunset, they made their way towards the nature park.

First up was the Bird Presentation where they saw colourful birds flying around and doing cool tricks! Esha thought they looked like flying rainbows, while Ishaan tried copying their chirps, much to the annoyance of Shanaya.

The Bird Presentation involved three different birds, each with their own trainer, dazzling the audience with different activities. Using the clues given below, match each bird with its trainer and the activity it did.

Clues

Birds	Trainers	Activities
Cockatoo	Arjun	Cycling
Falcon	Aditi	Flying through hoops
Macaw	Jhanvi	Painting

1. The bird known for diving at great speeds and using its sharp talons to snatch its prey amazed the crowd by flying through hoops.
2. The bird trained by Jhanvi did an activity which involved colour and a brush.
3. The Macaw was trained by Aditi.

Bird			
Trainer			
Activity			

Question 5

Animal Safari

After the Bird Presentation, the Shahs made their way towards a pond for their breakfast. Riding in an open jeep they saw different animals—like lions and giraffes—just hanging out doing their thing. Shanaya couldn't stop taking pictures and everyone was cheering whenever they spotted a new animal. They were really happy with how this short trip turned into an impromptu Animal Safari. They saw three different animals doing three different things.

Using the clues given below, match each animal with the activity they saw it do and when they saw it.

Clues

Animals	Activities	Order
Elephant	Drinking water	1st
Giraffe	Grazing	2nd
Lion	Sleeping	3rd

1. The 2nd animal the group saw is known as the King of the Jungle.
2. The 1st animal the group saw is the tallest land animal. It wasn't drinking water at the lake.
3. It was a pity that the 2nd animal they saw was sleeping in a large field under a tree.

Animal			
Activity			
Order			

Question 6

Breakfast with the Hippos

After a great start to the day, it was time for Breakfast with the Hippos! They were seated by the pond where they could see big, lazy hippos swimming in the pond. Ishaan's mouth couldn't stop watering as he went over the menu, whereas Mansi had to repeatedly ask Esha what she would like to eat. In the end, each child ordered a different item to eat and a different juice to drink. Watching the hippos splash in the water while enjoying their delicious breakfast felt like having breakfast with giants!

Using the clues given below, match each child with the food and drink they had.

Clues

Name	Food	Juice
Esha	Doughnut	Apple
Ishaan	Pancake	Orange
Shanaya	Waffle	Watermelon

1. The boy ate an item which usually has a hole in the middle.
2. Esha's juice was from a fruit which shares its name with a colour.
3. Esha did not eat the item which usually looks like a grid with many little squares.
4. Ishaan's juice was red in colour.

Name			
Food			
Juice			

Question 7

PETTING ZOO

The next stop was the Petting Zoo where they met friendly farm animals. The kids enjoyed the experience of feeding the animals. Along with taking multiple photos and playing with them, Shanaya made notes about all the information they were given about each animal.

Using the clues given below, match each animal with its name and the food the kids fed them.

Clues

Animal	Name	Fruit
Cow	Clarabelle	Apples
Horse	Kevin Bacon	Bananas
Pig	Seabiscuit	Carrots

1. Clarabelle's stomach is divided into four compartments.
2. Seabiscuit's face does not have a snout.
3. Kevin Bacon was not fed bananas.
4. The pig was not fed carrots.
5. The mammal that often wears shoes was not fed bananas.

Animal			
Name			
Fruit			

Question 8

Animal Show

The last stop for the day was the Animal Show. As the day started with birds doing tricks, it ended with sea animals doing various tricks. The kids clapped their hands and cheered for each animal, hoping that they would get them to repeat the tricks. It was the best show ever!

As the sun went down, painting the sky in beautiful colours, the Shah family said goodbye to the nature park. They were so happy, with hearts full of amazing memories. It was a day they would never forget!

Using the clues given below, match each animal with the trick it did and the number of times it did the trick.

Animals	Tricks	Numbers
Dolphin	Flip	2
Sea Lion	Slam dunk	3
Sea Otter	Waving to the crowd	5

1. The animal that breathes through a blowhole located at the top of its head did a trick five times.
2. One of the animals threw a ball through a hoop twice.
3. The sea lion waved to the crowd.

Animal			
Trick			
Number			

#1 Word Search

Animal
Kingdom

B	S	Y	C	V	C	T	X	A	W	Z	T
H	L	V	H	J	A	A	I	O	C	P	O
G	C	U	T	O	M	I	L	G	C	P	R
L	B	I	E	I	E	F	C	I	E	U	T
O	G	F	R	W	L	C	Q	Y	A	R	O
B	G	F	K	T	H	K	C	U	D	U	I
Q	N	F	E	E	S	A	P	J	N	O	S
C	J	F	E	X	R	O	L	I	A	T	E
R	I	T	A	J	M	F	M	E	P	M	B
I	A	L	Z	A	S	H	Q	H	K	D	M
H	N	G	E	K	I	Q	A	E	E	G	T
R	E	I	N	D	E	E	R	S	U	T	H

Answer the ten animal kingdom trivia questions and find the answers in the grid given above:

1) I am the world's largest mammal.
2) I am known as the Ship of the Desert.
3) I am the world's fastest land animal.
4) I quack.
5) I am the world's largest bird that cannot fly.
6) I am a black-and-white bear who loves eating bamboo.
7) I pull Santa's sled.
8) I am the world's largest wild cat.
9) I have the longest lifespan among all land animals.
10) I am the largest member of the dog family.

Question 9

NEW MOTHERS

Four sisters celebrated the joy of motherhood as each welcomed a precious baby boy into the world last year. With giggles and excitement, they gathered to share stories and cuddle their adorable little ones.

Using the clues given below, match each mother with her child and child's age.

Clues

Mothers	Children	Age
Aanchal	Maahir	12 months
Meghna	Rajvir	10 months
Eka	Shivansh	3 months
Shreya	Vivaan	1 month

1. Eka's child is older than Shreya's child.
2. Aanchal's child's age is more than the combined age of Maahir and Vivaan.
3. Shivansh's age is more than the combined age of Rajvir and Vivaan.
4. Meghna's child is the oldest.

Mother				
Child				
Age				

Question 10

PLAY DATE AT THE PARK FATHER'S EDITION

Four fathers bring their children—three girls and a boy—to the park for a play date. Bursting with energy and enthusiasm, they have a fun-filled day playing with the toys they brought from home. After all it wasn't going to be like any normal play date – it was going to be a super-duper fun extravaganza!

Using the clues given below, match each father with his child and the toy they brought to the park.

Clues

Fathers	Children	Toys
Anuj	Anaya	Bouncy Ball
Jehaan	Jahaan	Jump Rope
Kunal	Kiara	Hula Hoop
Mihir	Vaani	Stomp Rocket

- Jahaan is a boy. Anaya, Kiara and Vaani are girls.

1. Anaya did not bring the stomp rocket.
2. Kunal's daughter brought a jump rope with her but she is not named Kiara.
3. The bouncy ball belongs to Jehaan's son.
4. Anuj is Anaya's father.

Father				
Child				
Toy				

Question 11

PLAY DATE AT THE PARK MOM'S EDITION

Why should fathers have all the fun! After hearing all about the epic adventure of Play Date at the Park: Father's Edition, the moms are ready to show the dads how it's done. They've planned a rip-roaring water fight at the park.

Using the clues given below, match each mother with her child and colour of the water pistol each child brought.

Clues

Mothers	Children	Water Pistol
Ishita	Anaya	Red
Nishita	Jahaan	Blue
Vandana	Kiara	Orange
Zara	Vaani	Violet

1. The child who got the jump rope the previous time had an orange water pistol.
2. Zara's child had a red water pistol.
3. Mihir's child had a red water pistol.
4. Anaya's mother is neither Ishita nor the one with the violet water pistol.
5. Jahaan's mother is not Vandana.

Mother				
Child				
Water Pistol				

#1 Sudoku

1	2	3	
	3	2	1

	1		
			1
3			
		4	

Question 12

HANDYMEN

It was an unusually chaotic morning at Starlight Spire. The phone at the reception desk was ringing nonstop as three different apartments found themselves in dire need of handymen, each with their own urgent issues requiring attention.

Using the clues given below, match each handyman with his profession and the floor on which he was needed.

Handymen	Profession	Floor
Aditya	Carpenter	9
Nishant	Electrician	11
Parth	Plumber	13

1. Parth was not the one who was called to fix the wooden table.
2. Between Nishant and the one who can fix water leakages, one was called to the 9th floor and the other was called to the 13th floor.
3. Mrs Stevenson, on the 9th floor, needed some lights to be installed.

Handyman			
Profession			
Floor			

Question 13

Modes of Transportation

Once upon a time in a cosy little town, there were four brothers who were absolutely crazy about trains. From the moment they could crawl, they would chase toy trains all over the house, pretending to be operators.

Their love for trains came from their grandad. He was a legendary train engineer who had travelled the world on all sorts of trains, from mighty steam engines to sleek bullet trains.

As the years went by, the boys grew up, but their love for trains only grew stronger. When they finally became old enough, they decided to follow in their grandad's footsteps and become train operators.

Using the clues given below, match each brother with the type and colour of train they operate and their shift length.

Clues

Train Operators	Train Types	Colour	Shift Length (Hours)
Hrihaan	Bullet	Green	3
Rivaan	Monorail	Red	5
Vihaan	Subway	White	7
Yohaan	Tram	Yellow	9

1. The train which runs on the tracks laid on the streets is operated by either Hrihaan or Rivaan.
2. The operator who operates a train in an underground train network has a 9-hour shift.
3. The operator who has a 3-hour shift operates a green-coloured train which has a pointed nose, which allows it to reach very high speeds.
4. Between the subway and the tram, one is operated by Hrihaan and the other by Vihaan.
5. Yohaan has a 7-hour shift.
6. The red-coloured train is either operated by Rivaan or Vihaan.
7. The train which runs on a single rail instead of two is white in colour.

Train Operator				
Train Type				
Colour				
Shift Length (Hours)				

#2 Crossword Tiles

Clue: Fruits

Word Count: 4

Clues

N
A

L	E

G	R

B
A

O	R

N
A

P	P

P	E	S

N	G	E

Question 14

WAND SHOPPING

At the crowded Marvel Square market, four young students entered Abracadabra, a small corner shop known for selling the best wands in the region. It was not long before each of them was informed that they were not ordinary humans, but witches and wizards. They had been invited to join the Magicae Schola, one of the most prestigious schools of witchcraft and wizardry. Along with the invitation was a list of all the items they would need during this adventure. The first item on the list was a wand.

The four students were informed about the variety of cores, woods and lengths that wands come in. Using the clues given below, match each student with the characteristics of the wands they bought: wand core, wand wood and wand length.

- Jay Jain and Pranav Patel are boys, Anaira Agarwal and Mahek Mehta are girls.
- Dragons can also fly.

Clues

Name	Wand Core	Wand Wood	Wand Lengths (Inches)
Anaira Agarwal	Dragonpaw	Ebony	7
Jay Jain	Tortoisetail	Holly	9
Mahek Mehta	Sparrowclaw	Maple	11
Pranav Patel	Rhinoskin	Spruce	13

1. Between the two girls, one's wand had a core from an animal associated with the saying 'slow and steady wins the race' and the other's had a core from a magical legendary creature.
2. Jay's wand measured exactly two inches more than Mahek's.
3. Anaira's wand was made from a wood that shares its name with a sweet syrup.
4. The spruce tree was not used in either the shortest or the longest wand.
5. Jay's wand core came from an endangered species which has horns on its nose.
6. The two boys had the longest wand lengths.

7. The rhino skin core was housed in a wand made from wood from an ebony tree.
8. The wand which used wood from the spruce tree had a core from an animal capable of flying.

Name				
Wand Core				
Wand Wood				
Wand Lengths (inches)				

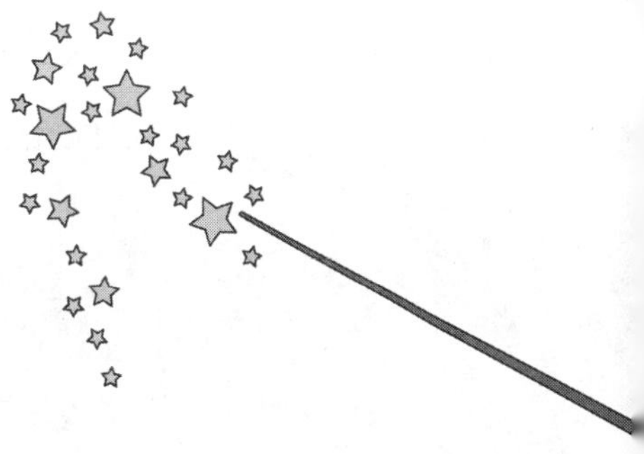

Question 15

SORTING

The four students were among the many who rode the magical carpets to arrive at the Magicae Schola. Just as they made way into the Great Plaza, the main gathering area in the school, they were informed that the sorting ceremony would begin shortly. Each house was led by a distinguished head teacher, who warmly welcomed the newcomers and offered guidance for the years ahead.

Using the clues given below, match each student with the house they were sorted in and the head of each house.

Clues

Name	House	House Head
Anaira Agarwal	Hobbledor	Aryan Chopra
Jay Jain	Centaurgaur	Kabir Khan
Mahek Mehta	Mogwair	Inaya Kumar
Pranav Patel	Titandon	Meher Maheshwari

1. Meher Maheshwari was the head of Centaurgaur.
2. Jay was either in Hobbledor or the house that Kabir Khan was the head of.
3. Mahek was either in Titandon or the house that Inaya Kumar was the head of.
4. Anaira Agarwal was in Mogwair whose head was not Aryan Chopra.
5. Mahek's house head was not Kabir Khan.

Student				
House				
House Head				

Question 16

PROFESSORS

It was the first day of term and all the first year students were excited to begin their magical adventure. As our four main characters were sorted into four different houses, they all had a different timetable for their classes.

Using the clues given below, match each student to the professor and subject of their first class.

Clues

Name	Professor	Subject
Anaira Agarwal	Aryan Chopra	Charms
Jay Jain	Kabir Khan	Potions
Mahek Mehta	Inaya Kumar	Mathemancy
Pranav Patel	Meher Maheshwari	Terraforming

1. Exactly two students' first class was taught by their head of house.
2. Aryan Chopra is the Potions master.
3. Inaya Kumar doesn't teach Mathemancy.
4. Kabir Khan is the Terraforming professor.
5. Mahek came first in the class taught by Inaya Kumar.

Student				
Subject				
Professor				

Question 17

QUADNET

As the term progressed, the school buzzed with excitement as students prepared for tryouts for the prestigious wizarding sport, Quadnet. The athleticism of our four main characters stood out, as they were selected for their unique talents on behalf of their respective house teams. Their contributions were immense, but at the end of the season, there could be only one winner.

Using the clues given below, match each student with the position they played and the final standing of their house.

Clues

Name	Role	Final Standing
Anaira Agarwal	Enforcer	1st
Jay Jain	Keeper	2nd
Mahek Mehta	Repeller	3rd
Pranav Patel	Scorer	4th

1. Jay's team finished behind Anaira's but before the team with the repeller.
2. The team that finished last had one of the boys in their team.
3. The team with the keeper finished 3rd.
4. The scorer led their team to the 1st place.
5. Anaira's team did not finish 1st.

Student				
Role				
Final Standing				

Question 18

Brewing Potions

With the end of term approaching, the students faced their final exams with a mix of nerves and determination. First up was the potions exam, where they meticulously brewed concoctions under the watchful eye of Professor Chopra.

Using the clues given below, match each student with the potion they were asked to prepare, the colour of the potion and the effect of the potion.

Clues

Name	Potion Name	Potion Colour	Effect of Potion
Anaira Agarwal	Elixir of Aóratos	Colourless	Invisibility
Jay Jain	Draught of Somnus	Gold	Love
Mahek Mehta	Felix Elixir	Purple	Luck
Pranav Patel	Potentia Amare	Red	Sleep

1. The four students are: Mahek, the Draught of Somnus, the gold-coloured potion and the potion that causes invisibility.
2. The colourless potion causes invisibility.
3. Pranav brewed the Felix Elixir.
4. The boy who came first in the class brewed the purple-coloured potion which does not make the drinker extremely lucky.
5. Anaira brewed the potion that is colourless.
6. Potentia Amare causes a feeling of love.

Student				
Potion Name				
Potion Colour				
Effect of Potion				

Question 19

Casting Charms

The final day of term was the charms exam, where they demonstrated their skill in wandwork and incantations under the guidance of Professor Kumar.

Using the clues given below, match each student with the spell they were asked to demonstrate, the colour of the sparks which came from their wands and the purpose of the spell.

Clues

Name	Spell	Sparks Colour	Purpose of the Spell
Anaira Agarwal	Aliquety	Blue	Disarming
Jay Jain	Exarmatius	Green	Levitation
Mahek Mehta	Vocare	Pink	Summoning
Pranav Patel	Zálisma	Yellow	Stunning

1. Between the two boys, one was asked to demonstrate the Disarming Charm and the other was asked to demonstrate the Stunning Charm.
2. Blue sparks are created when Vocare is used and pink sparks are created when Zálisma is used.
3. The girl who did the spell for levitation had yellow sparks fly from her wand.
4. Exarmatius is used to disarm an opponent.
5. Green sparks were created from either Anaira's or Pranav's wands.
6. Anaira was asked to demonstrate the Vocare Charm.

Student				
Spell				
Sparks Colour				
Purpose of the Spell				

#2

Word Search

European

Countries and Capitals

V	J	U	U	E	C	H	E	C	K	X	G
U	N	R	L	Q	J	N	E	Z	E	D	E
D	S	I	T	A	G	F	H	C	I	S	R
N	H	W	L	L	G	K	R	R	J	R	M
O	M	M	A	R	Z	U	D	A	K	W	A
D	I	M	Q	K	E	A	T	W	N	N	N
N	D	Q	H	Q	M	B	Q	R	A	C	Y
O	N	Z	J	D	L	I	S	B	O	N	E
L	G	Q	L	I	O	I	N	I	A	P	S
E	P	Y	O	T	Q	J	C	Y	T	H	D
X	I	W	Q	H	Q	W	Q	P	E	F	Z
W	A	G	E	Y	Z	E	S	I	R	A	P

Unscramble the 10 words given below to find 5 European countries and 5 European cities. Then, locate them in the grid given above.

COUNTRIES	CITIES
G N E L D A N	O L N O D N
F C N A E R	A S R P I
R G N E A M Y	N R E I L B
U L P G T A O R	L B I N O S
S N A P I	R M A D I D

Question 20

TMNT Scavenger Hunt

The makers of the new Teenage Mutant Ninja Turtles (TMNT) movie ran a promotional event in Euphoria City. They arranged an exciting four-part scavenger hunt. The goal of each of the four parts was to be the first to find one of the four Ninja Turtles hidden at different locations around the city. As luck would have it, each of the four teams—led by their enthusiastic and energetic captains—won one part of the hunt each.

Using the clues given below, match each team with their captain, the turtle they found and the location they found it.

Clues

Team	Captain	TMNT	Location
Clue Crusaders	Jia	Donatello	Hair Salon
Elite Explorers	Kaira	Michelangelo	Mall
Freaky Finders	Manav	Leonardo	Suprmarket
Treasure Troopers	Shom	Raphael	Train Station

1. The four teams are: the Elite Explorers; the team whose captain is Manav; the team that found Raphael first; and the team that found the turtle hidden at an establishment where people use hairdryers and brushes.
2. Treasure Troopers were the first to find the turtle hidden at a place which is also known as a grocery store.
3. Shom's team, the Clue Crusaders, were the first to find Donatello.
4. Manav's team was the first to find the turtle hidden at a place where people go to when they want to travel to different cities.
5. Kaira's team was the first to find Leonardo, hidden in one of the many shops at this place.

Team				
Captain				
TMNT				
Location				

Question 21

Birthday Parties

Five friends had the most amazing birthdays last year. From screaming their heads off on the many rides, to biting their nails while watching a classic superhero movie; from marvelling at the artifacts and antiques of the past, to enjoying the majesty of different land and underwater animals—each birthday party was epic! To make the moment even more memorable, each person received a stuffed animal as a birthday gift.

Using the clues given below, match each kid with the stuffed animal they got and the venue of their birthday party.

Clues

Kids	Stuffed Animal	Birthday Venues
Ananya	African Buffalo	Amusement Park
Dev	Elephant	Aquarium
Jasprit	Leopard	Cinema Hall
Myra	Lion	Museum
Siddharth	Rhinoceros	Zoo

1. The five kids are: Jasprit, the kid who got a stuffed African Buffalo, the kid whose birthday party was at a place where visitors can see different live animals, the kid who got a stuffed toy of the largest land animal and Siddharth.
2. Myra's stuffed toy had spots all over.
3. Dev and his friends sat on many rides on his birthday, with the Ferris wheel being his favourite.
4. Siddharth did not celebrate his birthday watching the new blockbuster.
5. The kid who got a stuffed toy of an animal with a name did not celebrate his birthday at a place filled with water tanks.
6. The kid who got the African buffalo stuffed toy celebrated his birthday looking at artifacts and antiques of the past.

Kid					
Stuffed Animal					
Birthday Venue					

Question 22

Clear Lake Academy Faculty

Clear Lake Academy is one of the most prestigious educational institutions in Euphoria City. Keeping up with its legacy of excellence, the school has hired four new teachers over the last few years with the aim of giving the students a more enjoyable learning experience.

Using the clues given below, match each teacher with the subject they teach and the year they joined the school.

Clues

Teachers	Subjects	Year of Joining
Mr Anand	English	2015
Mrs Banerjee	History	2016
Mr Chatterjee	Mathematics	2017
Miss Dutt	Science	2018

1. Between Mrs Banerjee and Miss Dutt, one joined the school in 2015 and the other joined in 2018.
2. Mr Chatterjee doesn't teach sentence formation.
3. Mr Anand joined the school in 2016.
4. Mrs Banerjee teaches a subject which involves a lot of numbers.
5. The last subject for which the school hired a teacher was a subject associated with laboratory experiments.

Teacher				
Subject				
Year of Joining				

Question 23

Inter-School Athletics Meet

At the annual inter-school meet, students from each grade represented their schools in different athletics events. This year was particularly good for Clear Lake Academy, as four of its students—each from a different grade—won first prize in their respective events, all of which were different. The school paper editor had been given information about which student from which grade won which event, but he seems to have misplaced it. However, he does recall some details from the article he was planning to write about the children.

Using the clues given below, help the editor determine which student from which grade won 1st prize in which event.

Clues

Students	Events	Grades
Aveer	100-Metre Dash	8th Grade
Kriti	High Jump	5th Grade
Shantanu	Javelin Throw	2nd Grade
Zoya	Shot Put	1st Grade

1. The four students are: Aveer, Zoya, the child who won the event which requires athletes to jump over a bar and the child who won the event which requires the athlete to throw a metal spear.
2. Usain Bolt is not one of the greatest athletes in the event Zoya won.
3. Kriti is in a grade higher than Zoya.
4. Shantanu is in a grade just one above Aveer.
5. The student who won 1st prize in the javelin throw was not the oldest.

Student				
Event				
Grade				

Question 24

Take Your Parent to School Week

Hey there, awesome students and super cool parents! Get ready for the most exciting event of the year–Clear Lake Academy's Take Your Parent to School Week! This is your chance to show off your amazing parents and learn all about what they do when they're not hanging out with you. It's going to be a blast!

Using the clues given below, match each student with their parent, the parent's profession and the day the parent came to school.

Students	Parent Names	Professions	Days
Sara	Divya	Flight Attendant	Monday
Tanmay	Gautam	Judge	Tuesday
Vedant	Rithika	Pharmacist	Wednesday
Zia	Yuvraj	Sailor	Thursday

Clues

- Gautam and Yuvraj are the fathers, Divya and Rithika are mothers.

1. The four students are: Tanmay, Gautam's child, the kid whose parent works on a ship and the one whose parent was the second to come.
2. Vedant's parent bought a gavel, which she uses often at work, to show to the class.
3. Sara's father came to school during Take Your Parent to School Week.
4. Divya was the first parent to come to school.
5. Zia's parent, who is part of a cabin crew, came to school on Wednesday.

Student				
Parent				
Profession				
Day				

Question 25

OLYMPICS

In the electrifying atmosphere at the recently held Olympic Games, four exceptional athletes won gold medals in different sports. Their remarkable achievements helped their country to perform well at the games on the grandest stage of them all.

Using the clues given below, match each athlete with the sport in which they participated, the country they represented and the total number of medals the country won at the games.

Clues

Athletes	Sports	Countries	Number of Medals
Akash	Boxing	Australia	3
Deepika	Gymnastics	New Zealand	20
Harsh	Swimming	South Africa	46
Khushi	Tennis	USA	112

1. The four athletes are: Harsh; the one who won a medal by doing a flip and somersault before landing on a vault; the athlete representing the country home to kangaroos and koalas; and the country which won 3 medals.
2. The medal won by the athlete for knocking out his opponent was one of the 3 or 46 medals won by that country.
3. The athlete who used freestyle, backstroke and breaststroke won all 3 medals for their country.
4. The Kiwi won a medal for his country on a grass court.
5. The athlete from the North American country helped her country win 112 medals.
6. Deepika won a medal by knocking out her opponent.
7. Akash is not the gymnast.

Athlete				
Sport				
Country				
Medal				

Question 26

TRAVEL DIARIES
FOOD IN ITALY

Meet Ayush, a super adventurous travel lover and storyteller! His amazing journey began in Italy, where he visited many cities. But the best part? Getting to eat all the yummy Italian food, like pizza and gelato, at various restaurants. It was like a tasty adventure for his taste buds which was made even more enjoyable by the wonderful staff at each restaurant.

Using the clues given below, match Ayush's favourite restaurant in each city, the hostess at that restaurant and Ayush's favourite dish at the restaurant.

Clues

City	Restaurant Name	Hostess	Food
Florence	Amore	Arya	Gelato
Milan	CinCin	Komal	Pizza
Rome	Pit Fire	Malvika	Spaghetti
Venice	Trattoria	Thea	Risotto

1. Ayush enjoyed a dish which is usually round in shape, cut into triangles at Amore.
2. Ayush used a gondola—a common mode of transport in this city to get to Trattoria where he enjoyed a frozen dessert.
3. Thea, who wasn't a Florentine, was the hostess at Pit Fire.
4. When Ayush visited Amore in the capital city, he was greeted by Malvika.
5. Between the restaurants where Arya and Thea were the hostesses, Ayush enjoyed a long string-shaped pasta in one and gelato in the other.

City				
Restaurant				
Hostess				
Food				

Question 27

Travel Diaries
Capital Cities Edition

Ayush's next travel assignment took him to five big capital cities around the world. But Ayush didn't want to experience these cities like any regular tourist. Instead, he went on exciting tours—like a bicycle tour, a helicopter ride, and even a zooming Segway tour.

Using the clues given below, match each city with the type of tour Ayush did and the order in which Ayush visited each city.

Clues

Cities	Tour	Order
Beijing	Cycling	1
London	Helicopter	2
New Delhi	Hop-On-Hop-Off Bus	3
Paris	Segway	4
Washington, D C	Walking	5

1. Between the city which is home to Eiffel Tower and the capital of India, one was the 1st and the other was the 2nd city Ayush visited.
2. Ayush took a helicopter ride in the last city he visited.
3. The capital where Ayush took a walking tour was visited after visiting the capital of the country which is home to the longest wall ever built.
4. The capital of France was visited after the capital city where he did a Hop-On-Hop-Off tour.
5. Ayush finished his trip in a city named after the country's first President.
6. Ayush did not take a Segway tour in Beijing.

City					
Tour					
Order					

Question 28

Travel Diaries
Famous Landmarks Edition

Ayush continued his stay at the United States, where he visited some of the most famous landmarks in the country. At each landmark, he bought a souvenir to remember the awesome time he had during the trip.

Using the clues given below, match each landmark Ayush visited with the kind of souvenir Ayush bought and the order in which he visited each landmark.

Clues

Landmark	Souvenir	Order
Hollywood Sign	Fridge Magnets	1
Mt. Rushmore	Keychain	2
Statue of Liberty	Postcard	3
White House	T-Shirt	4

1. Ayush visited the home of the President of the USA before the landmark where Ayush bought a fridge magnet, but later than the Statue of Liberty.
2. The 2nd landmark Ayush visited was either the White House or the Hollywood Sign.
3. Ayush bought a piece of clothing at the landmark which has the faces of 4 famous presidents carved on it, before he moved to visit the final landmark.
4. Ayush bought a keychain when he visited the landmark which was a gift from France to the USA.

Landmark				
Souvenir				
Order				

Question 29

Tourist Hotspots

Ayush didn't just stop at the most famous landmarks. He wanted to find hidden gems in the big cities he visited. He discovered secret spots that only locals knew about, making his adventure even more exciting!

Using the clues given below, match each city with the tourist attraction and the day Ayush visited that tourist attraction.

Clues

Cities	Tourist Attraction	Day
Los Angeles	Eclipse Sports Stadium	Monday
New York	Cobalt Sands Beach	Tuesday
San Francisco	Osotos Park	Wednesday
San Diego	Serenity Observatory	Thursday
Washington, D C	Walking Man's Art Gallery	Friday

1. Ayush saw the Statue of Liberty, among the many sites in this city, on Friday.
2. The city Ayush visited on Wednesday was not home to the Golden Gate Bridge, which he visited one day after he spent time jogging, playing catch with some kids, and having a picnic under the shade of a big elm tree.
3. Ayush relived his childhood by building a sandcastle on Wednesday.
4. Ayush enjoyed the many paintings and sculptures one or more days after he had visited the city that is home to the Hollywood film industry.
5. Los Angeles was not the first city on Ayush's itinerary.
6. Ayush lost his voice after cheering for his favourite football team in the country's capital.

City					
Attraction					
Day					

#2 Sudoku

		4	
	2		
		3	
	4		

	1		
			2
4			
		3	

Question 30

Mystery at Gupta Manor

Uh-oh! There's been a mystery at Gupta Manor, a big, old spooky house on the edge of Euphoria City. It's a real whodunit! Here's what happened: someone not-so-nice did something really bad. A new hotshot detective, who goes by the name Solvesalot is on the case. There are four suspects, each with their own story. They were all in different rooms when the incident took place. But here's the twist: each suspect had a reason to commit the crime, and they had their own favourite weapon they would have used—if they had got the chance.

Using the clues given below, match each suspect with the room they were in, their preferred weapon and their motive for committing the crime.

Clues

Suspects	Rooms	Murder Weapons	Motive
Ayesha	Bedroom	Dagger	Anger
Bhavika	Dining	Gun	Jealousy
Chinmay	Living	Poison	Financial
Dhruv	Kitchen	Rope	Revenge

1. The four suspects are: Bhavika, the one who was having a meal, the one who would have shot the victim and the one who was known to have expressed anger towards the victim.
2. Neither Dhruv nor the one who was in the dining room planned on harming the victim by adding something to his food.
3. The one who would have used a long, thick cord was seeking revenge.
4. Bhavika was in the kitchen at the time of the murder and was jealous of the victim.
5. The person who would have used the gun was not sitting on the bed.
6. Chinmay was under huge pressure to return a loan he had taken from the victim.

Name				
Room				
Weapon				
Motive				

Question 31

Multiple Murders

There's an air of doom and gloom in the otherwise happy Euphoria City. The police have found four bodies scattered at different locations across the city, all on the same day. Detective Solvesalot has been assigned the case and believes that the four murders are linked in some way. With the Chief of Police demanding swift action, Solvesalot is determined to piece together the puzzle and uncover the truth behind the interconnected murders.

Using the clues given below, match each victim with his cause of death and the location where the body was found.

Clues

Name	Surnames	Cause of Death	Location
Avyaan	Crawford	Strangling	Bus Stop
Farhaan	Daniels	Poisoned	Cemetery
Neeraj	Langford	Shot	Parking Lot
Rahul	Matthews	Stabbed	Vegetable Market

1. According to the medical examiner Mr Daniels died first; the second victim was found in the car park; Neeraj was the third to die and the fourth victim—the one who was stabbed—died last.
2. The strangling was done before Avyaan was murdered, which was done before Mr Crawford's murder.
3. Neeraj was shot.
4. Mr Matthews, whose body was found by a person while bargaining with a vendor, was not stabbed.
5. Rahul was either poisoned or his body was found in an empty grave.
6. Farhaan was not stabbed.

Order				
Name				
Surname				
Cause of Death				
Location				

Question 32

DIVING WITH ANIMALS

Ayush was on a super cool adventure! He wanted to see all kinds of amazing sea animals from around the world. So, he travelled to different countries. With the help of expert instructors who wore colourful gear, Ayush dove into the deep blue sea. They searched high and low, until they were able to spot exotic sea animals.

Using the clues given below, match each instructor with the country, the colour of gear they wore and the sea animal they helped Ayush spot.

Clues

Instructors	Countries	Gear Colour	Animals
Amrita	Australia	Black	Hammerhead Shark
Juhi	Indonesia	Blue	Penguin
Mira	Mexico	Green	Octopus
Sachi	South Africa	Red	Sea Turtle

1. The four instructors are: Mira; the one with whom Ayush dove in a place that is not just a country but also a continent; the one whose gear colour is associated with envy and money and the one with whom Ayush spotted a bird that cannot fly during his dive.

2. Mira told Ayush that the animal they swam with has three hearts.

3. After swimming with an animal which is named after the fact that its head is shaped like a carpenter's tool, Ayush enjoyed guacamole and nachos, the local cuisine.

4. Juhi was the instructor who made Ayush swim with a reptile and Sachi was the instructor who made Ayush swim with the penguin.

5. Between the instructors in the Asian and African countries, one's suit colour was associated with anger, while the other's was associated with royal blood.

6. Sachi, who did not wear a red suit, was Ayush's instructor in a country which has three capitals.

Name				
Country				
Gear Colour				
Animal				

Question 33

Activities at Famous Landmarks

Ayush's last assignment of the year was to write about some fun and adventurous activities he had done over the past week at some of the most famous landmarks around the world.

Using the clues given below, match each landmark with the activity Ayush did, and the time and day that he did the activity.

Clues

Landmarks	Activities	Time	Day
CN Tower	Bicycle Ride	4 pm	Wednesday
Golden Gate Bridge	Hands-Free Walk	5 pm	Thursday
Grand Canyon	Hiking Trail	6 pm	Friday
Great Wall of China	Toboggan Ride	7 pm	Saturday

1. Ayush either hiked or did the hands-free walk at a geographical feature formed by the Colorado river.
2. The activity at the telecommunications tower was done at 7 pm on either Thursday or Friday.
3. The hands-free walk was not done at the Grand Canyon or the landmark which is red in colour.
4. The hiking trail was not done at 5 pm.
5. Ayush visited the Golden Gate Bridge at 4 pm on Wednesday.
6. The hands-free walk was neither done at the landmark built by emperors to keep their land safe nor was it done on Thursday.
7. Ayush did not do the toboggan ride on a weekday.

Landmark				
Activity				
Time				
Day				

Question 34

FLIGHTS

It was the end of the year and Ayush was going through the many trips he took over the year. Among his many notes, he came across five boarding passes of flights he had taken.

Using the clues given below, match each flight number with its departure gate and destination.

Clues

Flight Number	Gate Number	Destination
1	1	England
2	2	France
3	3	Germany
4	4	Italy
5	5	Netherlands

1. The flight that flew to England did not depart from gate 1, 3 or 4.
2. Flight number 3 flew to the home of the Big Ben and the Buckingham Palace.
3. The flight that flew to the country also known as Deutschland did not depart from gate number 3 or gate number 4.
4. Flight number 4 did not fly to the country where croissants and macaroons are from or the country where pizza and gelato are from.
5. The flight departing from gate number 1 did not fly to France or Germany.
6. Flight number 1 or flight number 3 flew to a country where windmills are an iconic part of the landscape.
7. The flight that flew to the Netherlands departed from either gate number 2 or gate number 4.
8. Flight number 5 did not fly to Italy.
9. The flight departing from gate number 2 did not fly to England.

Flight Number					
Gate Number					
Destination					

#3
Crossword Tiles

Clue: Modes of Transportation

Word Count: 5

Clues

B	I
	P

L
I

C	L	E

O
P

B	U

T	R

S
H

T
E

A	I	N

H
E

C	Y

Question 35

VACATION PLANNING

Four close friends are seated around a big, cosy coffee table, having a loud and animated discussion. The topic of discussion—Where should they go for their vacation. With cups of hot cocoa in hand and smiles on their faces, each friend gives their suggestion. Some want to go to sunny beaches, while others dream of snowy mountains. It's like a big puzzle of fun destinations and cool times of the year!

Using the clues given below, match each friend with their dream vacation spot and the month they think would be perfect for the trip.

Clues

Name	Destination	Month
Akshay	Argentina	January
Anika	India	March
Manish	Japan	May
Maya	Switzerland	July

1. Neither Maya nor the one who suggested May suggested the country famous for cheese and chocolate.
2. The country suggested by the person who suggested January would not have Mt Fuji as one of its attractions.
3. Akshay did not suggest Switzerland.
4. March was not suggested by Anika or Maya.
5. Either Manish or Maya suggested the most populated country in the world.
6. Either Akshay or Manish suggested July, but neither of them suggested Japan.
7. Anika did not suggest Lionel Messi's country of origin and Manish did not suggest March.

Name				
Country				
Month				

Question 36

Executive Assistants

Five friends recently began their careers as assistants in different professions. To mark this, they decided to throw a fun party to celebrate their jobs and how hard they had been working. During the party they discussed each other's jobs, bosses and how long they've been doing it for.

Using the clues given below, match each person with their boss, the profession and how long it's been since they started their job.

Clues

Assistants	Bosses	Profession	Duration (Months)
Gaurav	Abhay	Architect	1
Ishan	Dev	Banker	2
Karan	Manav	Dentist	3
Rashi	Poorvi	Journalist	4
Suvidhi	Tina	Magician	5

- Rashi, Suvidhi, Poorvi and Tina are girls.

1. Between the two girls, one has worked for 2 months and the other has worked for 3 months.
2. Ishan has worked exactly 1 month longer than his friend who assists their boss in informing people about what is happening around the world.
3. Abhay's assistant has been with him since only 1 month.
4. The friend who has been helping her boss keep people's teeth and gums healthy has been doing so for 2 months.
5. A woman assists the man who advises people on financial matters and a male assists the lady journalist.
6. Rashi is very happy that she is gaining valuable experience working for Tina.
7. Dev's assistant helps him prepare designs and plans for builders.
8. Gaurav and Suvidhi have not worked for the longest or second-longest durations.

Assistant					
Boss					
Profession					
Duration (Months)					

Question 37

High School Reunion

It had been twenty years since five friends last roamed the hallowed halls of Clear Lake Academy. But as they reunited at their long-awaited high school reunion, it felt as though time had stood still. Gathered in the grand ballroom, they exchanged stories of their adventures after high school. Since graduation, each friend had moved to a different city to stamp their authority in different professional fields.

Using the clues given below, match each friend with the city they live in and their profession.

Clues

Name	City	Profession
Ayra Arora	Dubai	Builder
Farah Bansal	Johannesburg	Lawyer
Rohan Chadha	Moscow	Musician
Tarun Desai	Shanghai	Nurse
Vidya Emani	Tokyo	Teacher

1. The five friends are: Farah Bansal; the one who lives in the largest city in China; the one who gives advice on legal matters; the one who lives in the tallest building in the world and Rohan Chadha.
2. Vidya Emani looks after unwell and injured people with the utmost care but does not live in the Middle East.
3. Farah Bansal and Tarun Desai live in capital cities.
4. The friend who helps children become smarter lives in the capital of Russia.
5. Between Ayra Arora and Tarun Desai, one works at construction sites and the other works in the courthouse.

Name					
City					
Profession					

Question 38

EXTRA CURRICULAR ACTIVITIES

At Clear Lake Academy, learning goes beyond the classroom walls. Each student is required to sign up for one extracurricular activity.

Using the clues given below, match each student with the activity they signed up for, the faculty member who conducts it and the day it takes place.

Students	Activities	Faculty Members	Days
Aarika	Baseball	Mr Goenka	Monday
Bhoomi	Chess	Mr Haq	Tuesday
Chaya	Debate	Mr Iyer	Wednesday
Dhaval	Drama	Mrs Jaiswal	Thursday
Eklavya	Table Tennis	Miss Kamat	Friday

Clues

- Aarika, Bhoomi and Chaya are girls.

1. Strike and Home Run are terms in the sport Mr Iyer taught one of the boys.
2. Mr Haq heads the activity which takes place on Thursday.
3. Mr Iyer conducts an activity which takes place on a day before Bhoomi's activity.
4. The activity that requires formal arguments between two sides meets two days before Dhaval's activity takes place.
5. Miss Kamat is in charge of the extracurricular taking place on Wednesday.
6. Mrs Jaiswal is in charge of putting up the annual school play.
7. Chaya was the only girl who signed up for a sport.
8. Dhaval's activity takes place on the last day of the week while the drama club takes place on Monday.
9. Eklavya's extracurricular activity takes place one day before Bhoomi's.
10. Mr Haq taught an activity which requires a two-coloured racket.

Student					
Activity					
Faculty Member					
Day					

Question 39

Sports Scholarships

In the sunny halls of Clear Lake Academy, five amazing friends were celebrating something super exciting! They had all won special University scholarships for their favourite sports. But, even though they were happy about their big accomplishments, they were also a little sad. Why? Because they would be living in different cities.

Using the clues given below, match each friend with their new university, the city they're moving to, and the sport they will be playing.

Clues

Students	University	City	Sport
Aarav Lalwani	Crimson Peak College	Barcelona	American Football
Kavir Malhotra	Greenbecks University	Miami	Basketball
Reyansh Narayan	Oakland Technical Institute	Mumbai	Cricket
Vansh Oberoi	Moonstone Institute	Singapore	Rowing
Yug Parmar	Stonewall University	Sydney	Tennis

1. The five students are: Aarav Lalwani; Kavir Malhotra; the kid who is going to the city famous for the Harbour Bridge; the kid whose idol is Michael Jordan and the kid who won a scholarship for a sport played with an oval-shaped ball.
2. Yug Parmar, who frequently hears the phrase 'Game, Set and Match!' is not going to Oakland Technical Institute.
3. Neither Aarav Lalwani nor Vansh Oberoi is going to Oakland Technical Institute or Stonewall University. However, one of these four aims to follow in the footsteps of greats such as Sachin Tendulkar and Shane Warne by going to a university in the city whose symbol is the Merlion.

4. Kavir Malhotra got into Greenbecks University.
5. Vansh Oberoi, who is excited about visiting the Camp Nou during his free time, did not get the American football scholarship.
6. Aarav Lalwani is not the kid going to Moonstone Institute.
7. The American football scholarship was not given by the university in the city which is home to the Gateway of India..

Name					
University					
City					
Sport					

Question 40

Science Fair Projects

At Clear Lake Academy's Science Fair, bright young minds amazed their fellow students, teachers and parents with some amazing projects.

Using the clues given below, match each student with their project and where they were placed in the Science Fair.

Name	Surname	Project	Position
Aadya	Nair	Invisible Ink	1st
Hardik	Pandey	Mentos and Soda Fountain	2nd
Prisha	Rathore	Paper Rocket Launcher	3rd
Rishabh	Srivastava	Soda and Vinegar Volcano	4th
Saira	Tandon	Vegetable Battery	5th

Clues

- Aadya, Prisha and Saira are girls.

1. The five children are: Prisha; the Nair boy; the Srivastava kid; the kid who made the Mentos and Soda Fountain and the kid who came in 2nd place.
2. Either Rishabh and Hardik came in 2nd and the other came in 4th.
3. Saira finished before Hardik.
4. Hardik did not make the Soda and Vinegar Volcano.
5. The Rathore kid finished ahead of the kid who made the Mentos and Soda Fountain, who finished ahead of Prisha.
6. Hardik, the girl who finished 1st and the Nair kid made the Soda and Vinegar Fountain, the Paper Rocket Launcher and the Invisible Ink.
7. Hardik was placed either one position ahead of or one position behind the kid who made the Paper Rocket Launcher.
8. The Tandon girl was not Prisha.

Name					
Surname					
Project					
Position					

Question 41

Geography Presentation

Students in the eighth grade at Clear Lake Academy were tasked with creating a Geography presentation as part of their end-of-year assessment. Each student focused on a geographical feature from a different country.

Using the clues given below, match each student with the geographical feature, country and length of presentation.

Clues

Names	Geographical Feature	Countries	Presentation Length (Minutes)
Ritu	Glacier	Canada	5
Sneha	Lake	Nepal	10
Trishla	Mountain	New Zealand	20
Yuv	River	United Kingdom	25
Zaid	Waterfall	USA	30

1. Trishla's presentation was longer than both the presentation on the geographical feature of the country with the Union Jack flag and the one about an elevated portion of the Earth's crust.
2. Trishla's presentation was shorter than the student whose presentation was on the geographical feature of the country whose flag is very similar to the flag of Australia and the student whose presentation was about a body of dense ice.
3. Zaid's presentation was twice as long as the one on the freshwater stream but only half as long as the one on a geographical feature of the country whose flag is known as Stars and Stripes.
4. The presentation on the geographical feature of the country whose flag is the only one not shaped as a rectangle or square was 10 minutes shorter than the one about a body of water surrounded by land, which itself was 10 minutes shorter than Yuv's presentation.
5. Sneha's presentation on the UK was the shortest, while the presentation about the waterfall was the longest.
6. The presentation on the geographical feature of the country whose flag has a large maple leaf lasted 25 minutes.

Name					
Geographical Feature					
Country					
Length					

#3 Word Search

Geography

Trivia

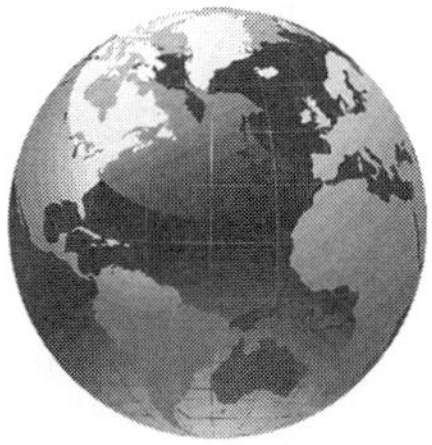

A	R	B	W	R	H	O	V	P	B	A	M
H	I	N	W	K	O	G	A	O	H	A	J
D	U	S	O	P	L	K	R	Q	Q	P	X
A	B	O	A	Z	L	K	W	N	I	L	E
I	R	W	N	C	A	N	I	S	U	U	H
S	U	H	C	Q	N	M	A	N	B	F	C
S	I	O	V	E	D	H	A	R	D	I	R
U	F	J	P	O	A	Q	Z	E	F	I	U
R	T	S	E	R	E	V	E	I	A	C	A
L	Q	Q	A	R	D	V	C	S	W	H	M
N	D	N	S	A	Y	A	L	A	M	I	H
O	N	W	N	U	P	E	R	G	W	L	Z

Answer the ten geography trivia questions and find the answers in the grid given above:

1) Alternate name of the Netherlands: _____
2) Largest desert in the world: _____ Desert
3) Highest mountain in the world: Mount _____
4) Largest continent in the world: _____
5) Largest country in the world: _____
6) Largest ocean in the world: _____
7) Longest river in the world: _____
8) Most populated country in the world: _____
9) Tallest mountain range in the world: The _____
10) River that flows through the rainforest in Brazil: ____

Question 42

Landmark Restoration

Hello there, boss of the world's biggest maintenance company! You've got a major responsibility on your shoulders—looking after some of the most iconic landmarks across the globe! But no stress—you've got it all under control. Several top companies are eager to step in and help restore these famous sites and after careful consideration, you've chosen the perfect ones for the job.

Using the clues given below, match each company with the landmark they'll fix, the kind of damage they'll repair, and how long it'll take.

Clues

Activity	Landmark	Damage	Repair Time (Months)
Cement Heads	Burj Khalifa	Faulty Plumbing	3
Master Builders	Colosseum	Fire Damage	6
Superior Structures	Eiffel Tower	Peeling Paint	9
The Good Construction Co	Sydney Opera House	Water Damage	12

1. The four landmarks are: the tallest building in the world; the one that had water damage; the one that was going to be repaired by Cement Heads and the one whose restoration would take 6 months.
2. Cement Heads were not hired to work on the symbol of Paris and Superior Structures were not hired to repair water damage.
3. Between Cement Heads and Master Builders, one estimated 12 months to complete the work and the other was hired for painting work.
4. The landmark which had fire damage was neither the Burj Khalifa nor the one famous for its white roof.
5. Master Builders would take a longer time than Cement Heads.
6. Superior Structures would take 9 months to complete the restoration.
7. The landmark in Rome had suffered water damage.

Name				
Landmark				
Damage				
Repair Time (Months)				

Question 43

CHORES

Naina Sharma was feeling a bit frustrated. She had five children and they were being a little lazy today. There were so many chores to do and they had to get ready for dinner with the Johnson family. Naina needed some help and she needed it fast!

She called her children over and told them that each of them had to do one chore before dinner. But here's the tricky part: every chore was in a different location, and each child had to use a different mode of transportation to get there.

Using the clues given below, match each kid with the place they went to, the mode of transport they used and the time it took to reach their destination.

Clues

Names	Places	Mode of Transport	Time (Minutes)
Hrithik	Bank	Bicycle	10
Irfan	Laundromat	Car	25
Neha	Library	Motorbike	30
Priya	Pharmacy	Taxi	35
Udit	Supermarket	Tuk-Tuk	50

1. Udit, the one who went to return books to avoid a late fee, had to travel at least 15 minutes more than the one who travelled by a form of public transport which has three wheels.
2. Neha drove herself in the family's four–wheeler, but not for 25 minutes.
3. Neither Priya nor the sibling who went to deposit money travelled for 10 minutes.
4. Irfan took 35 minutes to reach his destination.
5. The one who had to wash, dry and fold items had to travel 30 minutes.
6. The sibling who carried a prescription did not require any form of fuel.
7. The one who travelled for 10 minutes wore a helmet and had to stop to fill the fuel.

Sibling					
Place					
Mode of Transport					
Time (Minutes)					

Question 44

World Weightlifting Championship

The World Weightlifting Championship was super thrilling this year! Five fantastic contestants showed off their super strength and tried to lift really heavy weights.

Using the clues given below, match each contestant with her coach, the country she represented and the weight she lifted.

Clues

Names	Surnames	Coaches	Countries	Weight Lifted (Kilos)
Alaya	Bumrah	Kshitij	Brazil	20
Disha	Dhoni	Raghav	Canada	25
Pranaya	Ganguly	Sachin	Russia	40
Raha	Kohli	Uday	South Africa	45
Sayesha	Singh	Vaibhav	USA	50

1. The five contestants are: Raha Bumrah; the one who lifted the second lightest weight; Miss Dhoni; the one who was coached by Kshitij and the one who was coached by Raghav.
2. The contestant who lifted 25 kilos represented the 2nd largest country, in terms of area, in the world.
3. Miss Kohli was coached by Vaibhav.
4. The contestant who was coached by Sachin lifted twice the weight that Raha Bumrah lifted.
5. Alaya Singh represented the largest South American country.
6. The contestant representing Russia lifted the highest weight.
7. Sayesha lifted more than the contestant from Nelson Mandela's home country but less than the contestant coached by Sachin.
8. Pranaya, who represented the largest country in the world, was not coached by Raghav.

Name					
Surname					
Coach					
Country					
Weight Lifted (Kilos)					

Question 45

StarQuest
Mission to the Planets

StarQuest is launching five incredible space missions to explore distant planets!

Each mission has a unique leader, a specific goal and a launch site located in one of five different countries.

Clues

Project Leader	Mission Objective	Launch Site	Planet
Garima	Mapping Surface Terrain (MST)	China	Mars
Rishika	Analysing Planetary Atmosphere (APA)	Germany	Neptune
Jesal	Possibility of Life (POL)	Eiffel Tower	Saturn
Aditya	Study Storm Dynamics (SSD)	USA	Jupiter
Harsh	Measure Temperature Changes (MTC)	Japan	Mercury

1. Garima was leading an expedition to map the surface terrain (MST) of the Red Planet.
2. Rishika's expedition would have her exploring a planet that's deep blue.
3. The expedition launching from the home of the Eiffel Tower was to a planet known for its rings.
4. Aditya's expedition would launch from the country whose nickname is 'Uncle Sam' and go to the biggest planet in our solar system.
5. The expedition launching from the Land of the Rising Sun is to measure the temperature changes (MTC) at the planet closest to the Sun.
6. Between the expeditions launching from Japan and the USA, one was headed by Harsh and the other was headed by Aditya.
7. Neither Rishika's expedition nor the expedition launching from the country home to pandas would deal with exploring the possibility of life (POL) on another planet.
8. Aditya's expedition would have him study storm dynamics (SSD).

Project Leader					
Mission Objective					
Launch Site					
Planet					

#3

Sudoku

4	3		
		1	3

	3		
2		1	
	1		2
		3	

Answers

Logic Grids

1

Boy	Lakshya	Jeh	Hridaan
Flavour	Salted	Caramel	Cheese
Size	Small	Medium	Large

2

Friend	Brinda	Alia	Chandni
Wine	Choc Malt	Vanilla Special	Strawberry Marshmallow
Cheese	Cheese	Peri Peri	Plain

3

Person	Mr Blue	Mr Red	Mr Yellow
Clothes Colour	Yellow	Blue	Red
Hat Colour	Red	Yellow	Blue

4

Bird	Cockatoo	Falcon	Macaw
Trainer	Jhanvi	Arjun	Aditi
Activity	Painting	Flying through hoops	Cycling

Animal	Giraffe	Lion	Elephant
Activity	Grazing	Sleeping	Drinking water
Order	1st	2nd	3rd

6

Name	Esha	Ishaan	Shanaya
Food	Pancake	Doughnut	Waffle
Juice	Orange	Watermelon	Apple

7

Animal	Cow	Horse	Pig
Name	Clarabelle	Seabiscuit	Kevin Bacon
Fruit	Banana	Carrots	Apples

8

Animal	Dolphin	Sea Lion	Sea Otter
Trick	Flip	Waving to the crowd	Slam dunk
Number	5	3	2

9

Mother	Shreya	Eka	Aanchal	Meghna
Child	Vivaan	Maahir	Rajvir	Shivansh
Age (Months)	1 month	3 months	10 months	12 months

10

Father	Anuj	Jehaan	Kunal	Mihir
Child	Anaya	Jahaan	Vaani	Kiara
Toy	Hula Hoop	Bouncy Ball	Jump Rope	Stomp Rocket

11

Mother	Ishita	Nishita	Vandana	Zara
Child	Vaani	Jahaan	Anaya	Kiara
Water Pistol Colour	Orange	Violet	Blue	Red

12

Handyman	Nishtant	Parth	Aditya
Profession	Electrician	Plumber	Carpenter
Floor	9th	13th	11th

13

Train Operator	Rivaan	Hrihaan	Yohaan	Vihaan
Train Type	Bullet	Tram	Monorail	Subway
Colour	Green	Yellow	White	Red
Shift Length (Hours)	3	5	7	9

14

Student	Anaira Agarwal	Mahek Mehta	Jay Jain	Pranav Patel
Wand Core	Tortoisetail	Dragonpaw	Rhinoskin	Sparrowclaw
Wand Wood	Maple	Spruce	Ebony	Holly
Wand Length (Inches)	7	9	11	13

15

Student	Anaira Agarwal	Jay Jain	Mahek Mehta	Pranav Patel
House	Mogwair	Hobbledor	Titandon	Centaurgaur
House Head	Kabir Khan	Inaya Kumar	Aryan Chopra	Meher Maheshwari

16

Student	Anaira Agarwal	Jay Jain	Mahek Mehta	Pranav Patel
Subject	Terraforming	Potions	Charms	Mathemancy
Professor	Kabir Khan	Aryan Chopra	Inaya Kumar	Meher Maheshwari

17

Student	Anaira Agarwal	Jay Jain	Mahek Mehta	Pranav Patel
Role	Enforcer	Keeper	Scorer	Repeller
Final Standing	2nd	3rd	1st	4th

18

Student	Anaira Agarwal	Jay Jain	Mahek Mehta	Pranav Patel
Potion	Elixir of Aóratos	Draught of Somnus	Potentia Amare	Felix Elixir
Potion Colour	Colourless	Purple	Red	Gold
Potion Effect	Invisibility	Sleep	Love	Luck

19

Student	Anaira Agarwal	Jay Jain	Mahek Mehta	Pranav Patel
Potion	Vocare	Zálisma	Aliquety	Exarmatius
Potion Colour	Blue	Pink	Yellow	Green
Potion Effect	Summoning	Stunning	Levitation	Disarming

20

Team	Clue Crusaders	Elite Explorers	Freaky Finders	Treaure Troopers
Captain	Shom	Kaira	Manav	Jia
TMNT	Donatello	Leonardo	Michelangelo	Raphael
Location	Hair Salon	Mall	Train Station	Supermarket

21

Kid	Ananya	Dev	Jasprit	Myra	Siddharth
Stuffed Animal	African Buffalo	Elephant	Lion	Leopard	Rhinoceros
Birthday Venue	Museum	Amusement Park	Cinema Hall	Zoo	Aquarium

22

Teacher	Mrs. Banerjee	Mr. Anand	Mr. Chatterjee	Miss Dutt
Subject	Mathematics	English	History	Science
Year of Joining	2015	2016	2017	2018

23

Student	Aveer	Shantanu	Zoya	Kriti
Event	100-Metre Dash	Javelin Throw	Shot Put	High Jump
Grade	1st	2nd	5th	8th

24

Student	Tanmay	Vedant	Zia	Sara
Parent	Divya	Rithika	Gautam	Yuvraj
Profession	Pharmacist	Judge	Flight Attendant	Sailor
Day	Monday	Tuesday	Wednesday	Thursday

25

Athlete	Akash	Deepika	Harsh	Khushi
Sport	Swimming	Boxing	Tennis	Gymnastics
Country	South Africa	Australia	New Zealand	USA
Medals	3	46	20	112

26

City	Florence	Milan	Rome	Venice
Restaurant	CinCin	Pit Fire	Amore	Trattoria
Hostess	Komal	Thea	Malvika	Arya
Food	Risotto	Spaghetti	Pizza	Gelato

27

City	New Delhi	Paris	Beijing	London	Washington, D C
Tour	Hop-On-Hop-Off	Segway	Cycling	Walking	Helicopter
Order	1	2	3	4	5
Country	India	France	China	UK/ England	USA

28

Landmark	Statue of Liberty	White House	Mt. Rushmore	Hollywood Sign
Souvenir	Keychain	Postcard	T-Shirt	Fridge Magnet
Order	1	2	3	4

29

City	San Diego	San Francisco	Los Angeles	Washington, D C	New York
Attraction	Osotos Park	Serenity Observatory	Cobalt Sands Beach	Eclipse Sports Stadium	Walking Man's Art Gallery
Day	Monday	Tuesday	Wednesday	Thursday	Friday

30

Suspect	Ayesha	Bhavika	Chinmay	Dhruv
Room	Dining	Kitchen	Living	Bedroom
Weapon	Rope	Poison	Gun	Dagger
Motive	Revenge	Jealousy	Financial	Anger

31

Order	1	2	3	4
Name	Farhaan	Avyaan	Neeraj	Rahul
Surname	Daniels	Langford	Matthews	Crawford
Cause of Death	Strangling	Poisoned	Shot	Stabbing
Location	Bus Stop	Parking	Vegetable Market	Cemetery

32

Name	Amrita	Juhi	Mira	Sachi
Country	Mexico	Australia	Ecuador	South Africa
Gear Colour	Green	Black	Red	Blue
Animal	Hammerhead Shark	Sea Turtle	Octopus	Penguin

33

Activity	Bicycle Ride	Hiking Trail	Hands Free Walk	Toboggan Ride
Landmark	Golden Gate Bridge	Grand Canyon	CN Tower	Great Wall of China
Time	4.00 PM	6:00 PM	7:00 PM	5:00 PM
Day	Wednesday	Thursday	Friday	Saturday

34

Flight Number	1	2	3	4	5
Gate Number	4	1	5	2	3
Destination	Netherlands	Italy	England	Germany	France

35

Name	Maya	Akshay	Anika	Manish
Country	India	Argentina	Japan	Switzerland
Month	January	March	May	July

36

Assistant	Gaurav	Rashi	Suvidhi	Karan	Ishan
Boss	Abhay	Tina	Manav	Poorvi	Dev
Profession	Magician	Dentist	Banker	Journalist	Architect
Duration (Months)	1	2	3	4	5

37

Name	Ayra Arora	Farah Bansal	Rohan Chadha	Tarun Desai	Vidya Emani
City	Dubai	Moscow	Johannesburg	Tokyo	Shanghai
Profession	Builder	Teacher	Musician	Lawyer	Nurse

38

Student	Aarika	Eklavya	Bhoomi	Chaya	Dhaval
Activity	Drama	Baseball	Debate	Table Tennis	Chess
Faculty Member	Mrs Jaiswal	Mr Iyer	Miss Kamat	Mr Haq	Mr Goenka
Day	Monday	Tuesday	Wednesday	Thursday	Friday

39

Name	Aarav Lalwani	Kavir Malhotra	Reyansh Narayan	Vansh Oberoi	Yug Parmar
University	Crimson Peak College	Greenbecks University	Oakland Technical University	Moonstone Institute	Stonewall University
City	Singapore	Mumbai	Miami	Barcelona	Sydney
Sport	Cricket	Rowing	American Football	Basketball	Tennis

40

Name	Saira	Hardik	Aadya	Rishabh	Prisha
Surname	Srivastava	Rathore	Tandon	Nair	Pandey
Project	Paper Rocket Launcher	Invisible Ink	Mentos and Soda Fountain	Soda and Vinegar Volcano	Vegetable Battery
Position	1st	2nd	3rd	4th	5th

41

Name	Sneha	Zaid	Trishla	Ritu	Yuv
Geographical Feature	River	Mountain	Lake	Glacier	Waterfall
Country	United Kingdom	Nepal	USA	Canada	New Zealand
Length	5	10	20	25	30

42

Name	Sydney Opera House	Eiffel Tower	Burj Khalifa	Colosseum
Landmark	Peeling Paint	Fire Damage	Faulty Plumbing	Water Damage
Damage	Cement Heads	The Good Construction Co	Superior Structures	Master Builders
Repair Time (Months)	3	6	9	12

43

Sibling	Hrithik	Priya	Neha	Irfan	Udit
Place	Supermarket	Pharmacy	Laundromat	Bank	Library
Mode of Transport	Motorbike	Bicycle	Car	Tuk-Tuk	Taxi
Time	10	25	30	35	50

44

Name	Raha	Sayesha	Disha	Alaya	Pranaya
Surname	Bumrah	Kohli	Dhoni	Singh	Ganguly
Coach	Uday	Vaibhav	Sachin	Raghav	Kshitij
Country	South Africa	Canada	USA	Brazil	Russia
Weight Lifted (Kgs)	20	25	40	45	50

45

Project Leader	Aditya	Garima	Harsh	Jesal	Rishika
Mission Objective	Study Storm Dynamics (SSD)	Mapping Surface Terrain (MST)	Measure Temperature Changes (MTC)	Possibility of Life (POL)	Analysing Planetary Atmosphere (APA)
Launch Site	USA	China	Japan	France	Germany
Planet	Jupiter	Mars	Mercury	Saturn	Neptune

SHONIT BARADIA

Crossword Tiles

		B			
Y	E	L	L	O	W
		U			
	R	E	D		

		B				
O	R	A	N	G	E	
		N				
		A	P	P	L	E
		N				
G	R	A	P	E	S	

					H			
					E			
B	U	S			L			
		H			I			
	B	I	C	Y	C	L	E	
		P			O			
					P			
					T			
					E			
				T	R	A	I	N

Sudoku

Sudoku #1:

3	4	1	2
1	2	3	4
4	3	2	1
2	1	4	3

2	1	3	4
4	3	2	1
3	4	1	2
1	2	4	3

Sudoku #2:

1	3	4	2
4	2	1	3
2	1	3	4
3	4	2	1

2	1	4	3
3	4	1	2
4	2	3	1
1	3	2	4

Sudoku #3:

4	3	2	1
1	2	3	4
3	1	4	2
2	4	1	3

1	3	2	4
2	4	1	3
3	1	4	2
4	2	3	1

SHONIT BARADIA

Word Search

Animal Kingdom

B	S	Y	C	V	C	T	X	A	W	Z	T
H	L	V	H	J	A	A	I	O	C	P	O
G	C	U	T	O	M	I	L	G	C	P	R
L	B	I	E	I	E	F	C	I	E	U	T
O	G	F	R	W	L	C	Q	Y	A	R	O
B	G	F	K	T	H	K	C	U	D	U	I
Q	N	F	E	E	S	A	P	J	N	O	S
C	J	F	E	X	R	O	L	I	A	T	E
R	I	T	A	J	M	F	M	E	P	M	B
I	A	L	Z	A	S	H	Q	H	K	D	M
H	N	G	E	K	I	Q	A	E	E	G	T
R	E	I	N	D	E	E	R	S	U	T	H

European Countries and Cities

V	J	U	U	E	C	H	E	C	K	X	G
U	N	R	L	Q	J	N	E	Z	E	D	E
D	S	I	T	A	G	F	H	C	I	S	R
N	H	W	L	L	G	K	R	R	J	R	M
O	M	M	A	R	Z	U	D	A	K	W	A
D	I	N	Q	K	E	A	T	W	N	N	N
N	D	Q	H	Q	M	B	Q	R	A	C	Y
O	N	Z	J	D	L	I	S	B	O	N	E
L	G	Q	L	I	O	I	N	I	A	P	S
E	P	Y	O	T	Q	J	C	Y	T	H	D
X	I	W	Q	H	Q	W	Q	P	E	F	Z
W	A	G	E	Y	Z	E	S	I	R	A	P

Geography Trivia

A	R	B	W	R	H	O	V	P	B	A	M
H	I	N	W	K	O	G	A	O	H	A	J
D	U	S	O	P	L	K	R	Q	Q	P	X
A	B	O	A	Z	L	K	W	N	I	L	E
I	R	W	N	C	A	N	I	S	U	U	H
S	U	H	C	Q	N	M	A	N	B	F	C
S	I	O	V	E	D	H	A	R	D	I	R
U	F	J	P	O	A	Q	Z	E	F	I	U
R	T	S	E	R	E	V	E	I	A	C	A
L	Q	Q	A	R	D	V	C	S	W	H	M
N	D	N	S	A	Y	A	L	A	M	I	H
O	N	W	N	U	P	E	R	G	W	L	Z